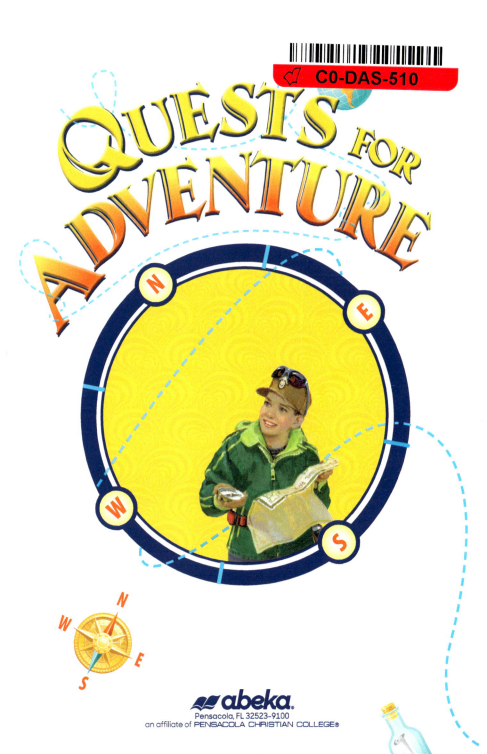

QUESTS FOR ADVENTURE

abeka.
Pensacola, FL 32523-9100
an affiliate of PENSACOLA CHRISTIAN COLLEGE®

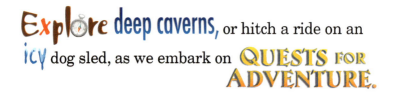

Explore deep caverns, or hitch a ride on an **icy** dog sled, as we embark on **QUESTS FOR ADVENTURE.**

By reading these exciting new stories about adventure and discovery, your student will learn the value of friendship, faith, kindness, and determination. A comprehensive review of special sounds from Phonics Charts 9–11 will further develop fluency in your child's reading. In addition to an emphasis on higher level thinking, this book will challenge your student with *Can You Guess* word puzzles and expand their literary understanding by introducing the concept of plot.

Quests for Adventure

Staff Credits

Managing Editor: Amy Yohe
Edition Editors: Tanya Harrington, Rachel Grosnick, Bethany Roberts, Juliane Roberts
Contributor: Laurel Hicks
Designer: Michelle Johnson
Production Artists: Susan Schmuck, Ruth Ann Chappell
Illustrators: John Ball, Dakotah Black, Bobby Dalrymple, Joyful Enriquez, Jeremy Gorman, Brian Jekel, Jamieson Jekel, Koby Jekel, Sarah Prelgovisk

Credits appear on p.154, which is considered an extension of this page.

Cataloging Data
        Quests for adventure--1st ed.
    154 p. : col. ill. ; 22 cm
    1. Readers (Elementary) 2. Reading (Elementary) III. Abeka Book, Inc.
Library of Congress: PE1119 .Q83 2017
Dewey System: 240

CNTENTS

Chart 9

-ing in pointing
kn in knot
gn in gnat
ang in bang
ing in king
ong in long
ung in strung
ank in bank
ink in wink
onk in honk
unk in trunk
wa in wash
a in adopt
y in baby
le in little
-ed in wanted
-ed in looked
-ed in played

Chart 10

wh in whale
wh in who
tch in patch
ear in ear
ear in bear
ear in earth
old in gold
mb in lamb
ew in flew
ew in few
-y in rainy
-er in bigger
-est in biggest
-ly in slowly
-en in sharpen
-es in peaches
ild in child
ind in kind

Chart 11

o in sh**o**vel
a in b**a**nan**a**
c in **c**ity
au in f**au**cet
aw in s**aw**
ea in l**ea**f
ea in thr**ea**d
ea in st**ea**k
ie in brown**ie**
ey in k**ey**
ey in ob**ey**
ph in **ph**one
ch in **ch**orus
ought in th**ought**
aught in c**aught**
g in **g**iant
dge in fu**dge**

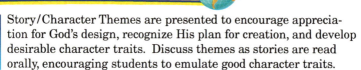

To Teachers and Parents

Story/Character Themes are presented to encourage apprecia-
tion for God's design, recognize His plan for creation, and develop
desirable character traits. Discuss themes as stories are read
orally, encouraging students to emulate good character traits.

Guide to Story/Character Themes

Compassion
  The Tenth Husky *4*

Contentment
  A Close Call *31*
  Bunny and His Airplane *77*
  Making the Best of It *91*

Quest

Bethany Roberts

Come follow me!
There's much to see
And no time now to rest.

Go pack your map.
Put on your cap,
And we'll go on a quest.

Perhaps out there
We'll find somewhere
A sloth upon a branch,

A drippy cave,
The biggest wave,
Or cowboys on a ranch.

We'll travel far
Where igloos are
And our wide world around.

When we've returned,
We will have learned
from everything we found.

Think About It!

Give the correct answer.

*From the poem, which quest would you choose?

*Questions marked with an asterisk require higher-level thinking.

1

-ing in pointing

talking	sitting	singing	seeking
shouting	telling	trying	calling

kn in knot, gn in gnat

know	kneel	knock	knight
knit	knead	sign	gnaw

y in baby

funny	puppy	happy	yappy
grumpy	slumpy	bunny	pretty

a in adopt

about	adult	agree	anoint
absorb	adapt	abrupt	afraid

Plot

The plot tells what happens in the story. A good plot has interesting characters, exciting events, and makes you wonder "what will happen next?" Just as God designed our world in a specific order, a story has order as well. A good story has a beginning, middle, and ending.

Words to Watch For

Sasha	huskies	whole
Luka	covered	happily

harnesses: *straps worn by a dog*

The Tenth Husky

Bethany Roberts

The igloo was glowing as the sun rose
that morning. Sasha got up on her feet,
and shook the snow off her thick, furry
coat. She was on a dogsled team of ten
huskies. Sasha loved to run with the dogsled team and explore. A fisherman was

their master, and he was very good to the dogs. He checked on every dog after each run to make sure none of them were hurt or ill. At the end of every day, he gave all the dogs a bite of fish.

"I must do something to thank the master," Sasha said. "Maybe I could find him the best fishing spot."

The rest of the sled dogs were still sleeping, but Sasha crept off. When she came to the woods, she began her quest for the perfect fishing spot. Just then, she saw a white rabbit dash into the brush. Sasha chased after it, and the rabbit ran even faster. They ran past trees and rocks topped with dusty snow. Finally, the rabbit dove into a hollow log and was safe. Sasha stuck her nose into the log, but it was too small for her whole body.

"You are too fast for me, Rabbit," she barked.

Then she looked up to see a wide river just past the log. The river was hard because ice had formed on the top. Out on the ice, there was a hole that had melted in the sun.

"The perfect fishing hole!" Sasha said.

With her fluffy tail wagging, she ran out to the hole in the ice. Then there was a cracking sound. Sasha froze. The ice around her was breaking. She stood very still. If she moved, she might fall into the cold river.

She began barking.

"Help, Master! Help!"

Back at the igloo, the fisherman began to wake up the sled dogs. He got the sled out and began to put the harnesses on the dogs. As he worked, he called each dog by its name.

"Good morning, Luka! Are you going to run fast today?" he asked as he rubbed Luka's neck.

Luka barked and wagged his tail.

"Rocky! Hello, old boy!" he said. "Jett! Alek! We're going to find some good fish today."

Then he stopped and looked around. He counted the dogs two more times.

"Where's Sasha?" he said to himself.

The dogs stopped barking and looked at the master. Then there was a howl from far away. Old Rocky howled back.

"That's her! Let's go!" the master called to the dogs.

The fisherman hopped on the sled, and the dogs ran as fast as they could into the woods. They followed Sasha's cry until

they came to the river. The master saw that
Sasha was afraid to move. When she saw
the master she hung her tail. She knew
she should not have left the team. As the
master started to walk to the ice, Rocky
tried to go with him. The master turned
and told the dogs to stay on the bank.

He got down on his knees and crawled
over the ice toward Sasha. While he
crawled, he felt the ice to see if it was thick.
When he could reach her, he tied her harness
to her shaking body and pulled her to the
thick ice. As soon as he was sure that the

thick ice could hold them both, he picked
her up in his strong arms and took her back
to the sled. The sled dogs barked happily as
they made their way to the river bank.

This time, the master did not let Sasha
pull with the other dogs. He laid her down
on the back of the sled and covered her
with a warm blanket. Then he called to the
barking dogs, and they pulled the sled all
the way back to the igloo. The next night,
the master tied Sasha's leash to a tree so
she would not run away, but she did not
want to leave the team any more. She was
happy to be safe and back with her master.

Parts of a Story

*1. Who is the main character in the story?

*2. Describe Sasha.

*3. What is the story mainly about?

*4. Number these sentences in the order that they happened in the story.

__2__ Sasha finds a good fishing spot for her master.

__4__ The team runs to find Sasha.

__5__ The master rescues Sasha.

__1__ Sasha chases after a white rabbit.

__3__ The ice breaks, and Sasha is afraid to move.

My Puppy

Aileen Fisher

It's funny my puppy
Knows just how I feel.

When I'm happy he's yappy
And squirms like an eel.

When I'm grumpy he's slumpy
And stays at my heel.

It's funny my puppy
Knows such a great deal.

Think About It!

Give the correct answer.

*What causes the puppy to act the way
that he does?

11

Words to Watch For

once   breath   slowly   except

think   whisper   knew

Shhh . . .

Bethany Roberts

"Cody!" I heard them call. "Hurry up! The game is starting."

My friends were outside waiting for me to play baseball with them. Brent had

told me that I was the best one at throwing the ball. He said that I just had to play on their team. I told him I had to go get my mitt, but then I remembered where I had left it.

"I can't go in there! Not now!" I said. I looked up and down, in the shed and in all the rooms in the house. There was no other mitt. I had to go into *that* room.

I took off my shoes so that my feet wouldn't make noise. I laid them outside the door, and took a deep breath. I turned the knob of the door as slowly as a snail would cross the sidewalk. I took a peek inside. Everything was silent and dark, except for a glow from a Noah's ark night-light on the wall. My heart gave a *thump-thump, thump-thump* as I took a small step into the dark room.

Nothing made a sound; so I took one more step. Everything was still. My tidy bed was on one side of the room and a crib was on the other. I looked around both beds, but my mitt was not near either of them. Then I spotted my baseball mitt on a desk in the corner. I began to tiptoe to the desk. When I was half way there, there was a loud *squeeeeeak!*

I held my breath and looked down at the floor where the squeak came from.

I had stepped on Caleb's rubber duck. A stir came from the other side of the room, and then a cry.

"Oh no!" I said and tried to think of what to do. I ran to the cry.

"Shhhh!" I said. "It's ok, Caleb! Please, don't cry!"

Baby Caleb did not even hear me. He just kept crying. Then I remembered a song my mom sang to me when I was a baby. I started to sing the soft, sweet tune, and soon Caleb was sleeping once more.

"Phew! That was close," I said to myself.

I took my mitt off the desk, and on the way back, I made sure not to step on the duck. I began to close the door without a sound. Before it was shut, I turned to whisper, "Sleep tight, Caleb."

When I did not hear a sound, I knew that he would.

Think About It!

Give the correct answer.

*1. Who is the main character in this story?

2. Why didn't he want to go into *that* room?

3. How did he get his brother to stop crying?

Words to Watch For

great   weigh   difference

Can You Guess?

Solve these word puzzles.

1 Which side of a pie is the left side?

2 What can fill a great big house
   yet still weigh less than a tiny mouse?

3 What is the difference between a dime
   and a penny?

4 I walked with the Lord
   in the cool of the day
And found out what happens
   when you disobey.
   Who am I?

1 the side that isn't eaten

2 air

3 nine cents

 4 Adam

Read Adam's story in Genesis 3:8–24.

Words to Practice

ang in b**ang**, **ing** in k**ing**

hang	bring	sang	thing
rang	wing	sing	twang

ong in l**ong**, **ung** in str**ung**

strong	rung	sung	tongs
lung	swung	stung	song

onk in h**onk**, **unk** in tr**unk**

donkey	shrunk	plunk	honking
sunk	dunk	skunk	chipmunk

le in litt**le**

giggle	wiggle	fiddle	puzzle
turtle	paddle	pebble	middle

ink in w**ink**

think	blink	sink	drink
rink	pink	link	shrink

The Morning Song

Bethany Roberts

The sun was starting then to rise
Up into the golden skies.
A rooster helped the sun along
By singing it a morning song.

"Cock-a doodle-doodle-doo!
The sun is rising. It is true!
Cock-a doodle-doodle-doo!
The sun is up, and I am too!"

A sunbeam peeked right through a crack
Inside a little Mouse's shack.
"Cock-a doodle-doodle-doo!"
The rooster sings. "The day is new."

20

Then the mouse rolled on his bed
And pulled the covers o'er his head.
"Oh, how I would sleep and snore,
If he would wait five minutes more!"

The Mouse's House

Pat Day

One time there was a woodland mouse

Who lived inside a funny house.

It had no doors, it had no floors,

The home of Mister Mouse.

22

The mouse's house was full of weeds and
   bits of grass and little seeds.
There were no chairs, there were no stairs,
And yet it seemed to suit his needs.

The little mousies had no bed, there was
   no roof top overhead.
There was no clock, there was no lock,
No lamp (they used the sun instead).
No roof, no lock, no clock, no doors,
No bed, no chairs, no stairs, no floors,
Where was the house of Mister Mouse?
Why, in a grassy field outdoors!

Think About It!

Give the correct answer.

   1. Where is Mister Mouse's house?

   *2. What other animals would likely
      live near the mouse's house?

Words to Watch For

woman	lived	loved
stories	lesson	counted
rejoicing	person	

The Lost Coin

When Jesus lived on Earth, He loved to tell stories. Some of these stories were a bit like riddles, and we can read them in the Bible. Jesus' stories were not only told for enjoyment; He used them to teach a lesson to the people He loved.

Sometimes, Jesus used small things to teach people about God. He even used something as small as a coin.

One of the stories Jesus told was about a lady who had ten coins. The story went something like this:

One day, a woman counted her coins and saw that one coin was missing.

"Did it fall on the floor?" she said to herself.

She knelt down on the floor and looked under the table, but she did not see the coin.

"Maybe it is too dark in here, and I cannot see the coin," she said.

She lit a candle and looked again. She still did not find the coin.

Then she said, "I will get my broom and sweep the house. Then I will find my coin." That is just what she did.

She swept every inch of her house. Finally, in one corner, she saw something round and shiny.

"My coin!" she said. She had found it at last. The woman cried tears of joy. She was so happy that she ran down the street to find her friends.

"Come see!" she said to them. "I found my lost coin!"

God seeks us just like this woman was seeking for her coin. He never stops loving us and calling us to Himself. The Bible says that in Heaven there is singing and rejoicing like we have never seen when just one person comes to God.

Luke 15:10

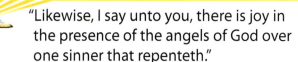

"Likewise, I say unto you, there is joy in the presence of the angels of God over one sinner that repenteth."

Think About It!

Give the correct answer.

1. What did the woman do when she found the coin?

*2. What does Jesus compare the coin to?

*3. Why do you think Jesus told this story?

 Read Jesus' story in *Luke 15:8–10*.

Weather

Aileen Fisher

Weather is full
of the nicest sounds:
it sings
and rustles
and pings
and pounds
and hums
and tinkles
and strums
and twangs
and whishes
and sprinkles
and splishes
and bangs

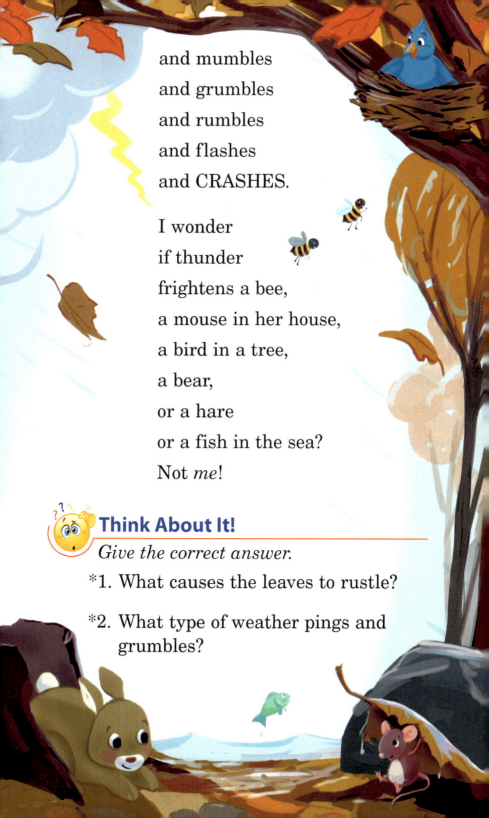

and mumbles
and grumbles
and rumbles
and flashes
and CRASHES.

I wonder
if thunder
frightens a bee,
a mouse in her house,
a bird in a tree,
a bear,
or a hare
or a fish in the sea?
Not *me*!

Think About It!

Give the correct answer.

*1. What causes the leaves to rustle?

*2. What type of weather pings and grumbles?

Words to Watch For

feathers   aren't

Bird Talk

Aileen Fisher

"Think . . ." said the robin,
"Think . . ." said the jay,
sitting in the garden, talking one day.

"Think about people—the way they grow:
they don't have feathers at all, you know.

"They don't eat beetles, they don't grow wings,
They don't like sitting on wires and things."

"Think!" said the robin. "Think!" said the jay.
"Aren't people funny to be that way?"

Think About It!

Give the correct answer.

*What is the poem mainly about?

Words to Watch For

only	where	hurried
nibbled	waddled	heard
scampered	pounced	sighed
skittered: *moved quickly*		

A Close Call

Milly was a chubby little mouse that lived in a hole in the wall. She was not happy eating only the small bits of food that she found on the ground. She wanted more, and she knew just where to find some.

One day Milly Mouse peeked out of her little hole just in time to see Tom Cat go out the screen door.

"Oh, good!" thought Milly. "Now I can hunt for more food to eat. Tom Cat is not here to chase me back into my hole."

Milly hurried to the table. Up the leg of the table she skittered, right to the top.

"Yum, yum," said Milly, as she nibbled on some food. "It will be fun to eat just as much as I wish!"

Milly Mouse ate and ate until she could eat no more. She ate ham, cheese, bread, fruit, and cake. Then down the table leg she went as she waddled back to her hole in the wall.

"That food was good, but now I am so full," she said.

Milly Mouse lay down on her little mouse-sized bed.

"I will just take a short nap," she said to herself.

When Milly woke up, she let out a loud moan.

She hurt from the end of her nose all the way to the tip of her tail.

"I think I ate too much food," groaned Milly. "Maybe I will feel better if I take a little walk."

As Milly crept out of the hole in the wall, she did not see Tom Cat sitting on the rug. Milly walked slowly to the door. Then she heard a sound. As she turned to look, she saw Tom Cat creeping after her. She scampered out the door with Tom Cat right behind her! Milly ran as fast as she could to a hole in the porch. She slid into the hole just as Tom Cat pounced. As Milly lay

panting, she could see Tom Cat trying to reach in with his paw.

"That was close," sighed Milly. "Next time I will not eat all that I wish, or Tom Cat just might eat ME!"

Think About It!

Give the correct answer.

*1. Who is the main character?

2. What was the *first* thing Milly did?

   a. went for a walk

   b. looked for some food

   c. took a nap

*3. What actions led to Milly's trouble?

What Do YOU Think?

*Why do you think the author wrote this story?

Can You Guess?

Solve these word puzzles.

1 What runs east and west;
And north and south;
Has many teeth,
But has no mouth?

2 What is worse than a giraffe with
a sore throat?

3 What kind of key does not unlock
a door?

4 I was a preacher
that stayed in a boat
And lived through a flood
because God made it float.
Who am I?

1 a saw

2 centipede with sore feet

3 a donkey, monkey, turkey

4 Noah
Read Noah's story in Genesis 7:7–17.

Words to Practice

wa in **wa**sh

swab	want	water	wasp
wander	swamp	walnut	swan

-ed in want**ed**

sprouted	counted	waited	darted
greeted	landed	planted	shouted

-ed in look**ed**

splashed	asked	chirped	dripped
dropped	helped	jumped	hopped

-ed in play**ed**

chattered	waved	dreamed	trickled
splattered	seemed	joined	turned

wh in **wh**ale, **wh** in **wh**o

wheel	where	which	whisk
whole	whose	why	whom

The Elephant and the Monkey

Deep in the jungle there once lived a monkey and an elephant who did not agree. The elephant thought of himself as being very strong.

"I can lift this big branch with my trunk," he said with great pride.

How proud he was!

The monkey thought of himself as being very quick.

"I can swing from branch to branch with great speed," said the monkey. "See how quick I am!"

"I think it is better to be strong," said
the elephant. "But since we cannot agree,
let's ask the wise old owl."

The elephant and the monkey came to
the home of the wise old owl.

"We can't agree," they said to the owl.
"Is it better to be strong or to be quick?"

"Do as I say, so that I may see which is
better," said the owl. "Go to that fruit tree

in the field across the river. Pick
some fruit and bring it to me."

Down the hill went the
elephant and the monkey.
But when they got to the
river, the monkey was
afraid to go across.

"I am strong," bragged the elephant.
"I am not afraid of the swift water. Get on
my head, and I will carry you across."

When they got to the tree on the other side of the river, they had another problem. The elephant tried to pick the fruit with his trunk, but the tree was too high. Then he tried to knock down the tree but he could not.

"I am quick," chattered the monkey. "I can swing fast from branch to branch, grab the fruit, and drop it to you."

That is just what the monkey did. The elephant picked up the fruit with his trunk. The monkey hopped onto the elephant's head, and back across the river they went.

"Which is better?" they asked the owl. "Is it better to be strong or to be quick?"

"Neither of you could get the fruit alone," said the owl. "It is not better to be strong nor is it better to be fast. It is better to work together and help each other to get the job done."

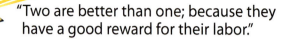

Think About It!

Give the correct answer.

Which was better—to be strong or to be quick? Why?

What Do YOU Think?

*1. What can you do to help others?

*2. Can you think of a job you would need help doing? Why?

42

Going Somewhere

Leland B. Jacobs

Let's go somewhere!

Where shall it be?

Out beyond the moon and stars?

Far across the sea?

Let's go somewhere

Not so far away,

The park, or hill, or any place

Where we can run and play.

Think About It!

Give the correct answer.

*Where would you rather go, somewhere far across the sea or somewhere near?

Mr. A. Giraffe

Helen E. Sheehan

Now A. Giraffe
    can never laugh,
And I will tell you why!
Because a giggle
    cannot wiggle
        Up so high.

And Mister A.
    can never say
"Oh, fiddle sticks!"
    nor "Fie!"
Because his talking
    tires of walking
        Up so high.

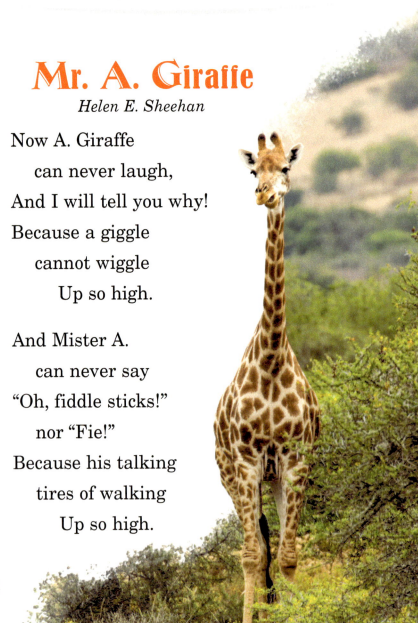

When Mister A.

   feels very happy

And starts to sing and shout,

A bubbly sound

    goes round and round–

      Never out.

So all these things

   just stay inside

And grieve about their lots,

Until poor Mr. A. Giraffe

   Breaks out in dreadful spots!

What Do YOU Think?

*1. Is the author's description of the giraffe true?

*2. Why does she think the giraffe has spots?

*3. Why do you think God made the giraffe with a long neck and spots?

Class Time in the Caverns

Bethany Roberts

Mrs. Bennet's class was taking a field trip one day. As the children sat in their seats on the bus, Mrs. Bennet told them what they were about to see.

"Today, we are going to the caverns," she said. "Caverns are like the caves we have been learning about in class. You will have a chance to see many of the things we have talked about. Everyone must stay very close to me and to our guide. We don't want anyone to be lost or hurt."

The children were very excited. They could not wait to see a real cave. When the

bus came to a stop, the children hopped
out of the bus one by one and lined up with
Mrs. Bennet beside a big oak tree.

"I don't see a cave!" Amy said.

"Where is it?" said Jack.

"You're standing on top of it," said a
lady in a tan suit. "It's underground."

The children all looked at the ground,
and some stomped their feet. The lady kept
talking, "We will have to go down some
steps to get to the cave. Follow me!"

They followed the guide into the welcome center and found the steps. Down they went into the caverns. It was dark, but lights lined the sides of the cave so they could see. They followed the guide down a path into the cave.

"Who can find a cave column?" asked Mrs. Bennet.

"There's one over there!" said Lily. She pointed to a column that had formed from water dripping from the roof of the cave. The class all looked at the stone column.

"Very good, Lily!" said Mrs. Bennet. "Do any of you remember what those are called?"

Mrs. Bennet pointed to some stone spikes hanging from the roof of the cave.

"I know!" said Max. "It's a sta-lac-tite."

"That's right!" the guide said. "Stalactite! You have a very smart class, Mrs. Bennet."

Mrs. Bennet winked at her class, and they gave her wide smiles. Just then, Jack saw something flutter.

"What is that?" he asked.

The guide looked where he was pointing. She grinned and said, "Oh, that is a bat!"

The children were afraid. "A bat?" they cried. "Will it hurt us?"

"No," the guide said. "Most bats are harmless. He is just letting you know that he is there."

"Bats are not very pretty, are they?" Amy said. "Why did God make animals like that?"

The guide had to stop and think. She looked at the bat and then back at Amy.

"Bats eat many of the bugs that are pests to us," said the guide. "If there were no bats, there would be bugs everywhere, and those bugs would eat the plants that grow food."

"That's right," said Mrs. Bennet. "And bats are like this cave, in a way. Some people say that they are not pretty, but we can still learn from them."

"Like what, Mrs. Bennet?" Max asked.

They walked down the path to get a closer look at the interesting animal.

"Do you see how the bat hangs upside down?" said Mrs. Bennet.

"That way, they can take off and fly much faster to get their dinner," said the guide.

"Wow!" said Lily.

Mrs. Bennet explained, "If you tried to hang upside down for as long as the bat does, it would hurt your body. But God made the bat so that he can hang for a long time and be just fine."

"It seems like God made the bat for a reason," said Jack.

"Yes, He did, Jack," said Mrs. Bennet. "God has a wonderful plan for all of His creation."

When it was time to get back on the bus, all the children were still talking about the things they had found in the cave. Mrs. Bennet shook the guide's hand.

"Thank you for taking my class down into the caverns," Mrs. Bennet said. "They learned many things today."

"Well, I learned something too, Mrs. Bennet," the guide said. "I learned that there is a great God who has a plan for all things."

Think About It!

Give the correct answer.

1. What three things did they find in the cave?

2. How did the guide hear about God?

*3. Why is it important that we learn about God's creation?

Romans 11:36

"For of Him, and through Him, and to Him, are all things: to whom be glory for ever. Amen."

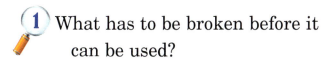

Can You Guess?

Solve these word puzzles.

1 What has to be broken before it can be used?

2 What kind of fish chases a mouse?

3 What comes down but never goes up?

4 When I was a grown man
   they searched far and wide
   with camels and riches
   to find me a bride.
   Who am I?

1 an egg

2 catfish

3 rain

4 Isaac

Read Isaac's story in Genesis 24.

Words to Practice

tch in patch

batch	hatch	scratch	stretch
switch	sketch	fetch	watch

mb in lamb

crumbs	thumb	comb	limb
plumber	numb	climb	tomb

ear in ear, ear in earth, ear in bear

beard	earn	gear	year
search	near	wear	dear
fear	pearl	learn	hear
early	pear	clear	tear

ew in flew, ew in few

chew	blew	knew	grew
screw	dew	new	mew

Rain Drop Splash

Alvin Tresselt

Drip drop *splash*!
Drip drop *splash*!
Went the rain all day.
Dripped from the shiny leaves,
Dropped from a rabbit's nose,
Splashed from a brown bear's tail.
Fell from a daisy's face
Trickled down tree trunks,
And *splunked* on a green frog's back!

Think About It!

Give the correct answer.

*What is a daisy's face?

56

Birdseed

Brod Bagert

It didn't work.

I planted birdseed in the ground

And wild weeds sprouted all around.

I know it sounds a bit absurd

But I couldn't grow a single bird.

The Broken Wing

Winter was coming. All the birds had flown south to wait for spring. All but one. That little bird had a broken wing and could not fly very far so he had to stay behind.

The poor bird looked all around. Where could he keep warm for the winter? At last he thought of the trees in the forest.

"Perhaps the trees will help me stay warm," thought the little bird. So he hopped into the forest. First he came to the trunk of a white birch tree.

He looked up and asked, "Pretty white birch tree, will you let me live in your branches until springtime comes?"

The white birch tree shook her leaves. They made a rustling sound as she said, "Dear me, I have to take care of my leaves. I cannot take care of a little bird. Go away!"

So the little bird hopped along until he came to a big oak tree.

"Big oak tree," said the little bird, "will you please let me live in your branches until springtime comes?"

"Oh, no!" said the big oak tree. "I cannot shelter you. I must get my new leaves ready for the spring."

The little bird hopped away until he
came to a willow tree.

"Oh, grand willow tree," said the little
bird, "may I live in your warm branches
until springtime comes?"

The willow tree waved her branches in
the soft breeze. "Oh, no," replied the willow
tree. "I cannot be bothered with you."

The poor little bird did not know where
to go. At last he came to a fir tree.

The fir tree saw the little bird and said, "You poor little bird. Where are you going?"

"I do not know," answered the little bird. "I cannot fly south, for I have a broken wing. I have been asking the trees to help me, but not one will give me shelter."

"You may live with me," said the fir tree. "Here is my warmest branch."

"May I live with you all winter?" asked the little bird.

"Yes," answered the fir tree. "I would like to have you stay with me."

"Thank you," chirped the little bird.

A tall pine tree that stood close by heard what the little bird said. "I am big and strong," said the tall pine tree to the fir tree. "I will keep the cold wind off the little bird while he lives in your branches."

"I will give him berries to eat," said a juniper tree which stood nearby. "My berries are good for little birds."

61

The little bird was cared for all that winter. When the other birds returned in the spring, he could fly. His injured wing was well once again.

Think About It!

Give the correct answer.

*1. What is this story mainly about?

*2. How did the first three trees act toward the little bird?

   a. selfish

   b. kind

   c. loving

 3. What happened after the fir tree offered to help the little bird?

Ephesians 4:32

"And be ye kind one to another."

lion

Homes

Ilo Orleans

A dog lives in a *kennel*;
   A pig lives in a *pen*;
A horse lives in a *stable*;
   And a lion in a *den*.

A chicken lives inside a *coop*;
   And goldfish in a *bowl*;
And sheep are happy in a *fold*–
   A mole, inside a *hole*.

The turtle lives inside his *shell*;
   The thrush lives in a *nest*;
And I live in a little *house*;
   For ME that is the best!

Jump or Jiggle

Evelyn Beyer

Frogs jump.
Caterpillars slump.

Worms wiggle.
Bugs jiggle.

Rabbits hop.
Horses clop.

Snakes slide
Sea gulls glide.

Puppies bounce.
Kittens pounce.

Lions stalk–
But
I walk!

64

Can You Guess?

Solve these word puzzles.

1 Floppy big ears and a wrinkled gray suit,
Rope for a tail and a funny, long snoot.
Which of the animals do I mean?
Just guess the largest you ever have seen.

2 Why is it so easy to weigh a fish?

3 What has hands but cannot clap?

4 I gave God the very best fruits that I had.
When He did not take them,
I then became mad.
Who am I?

1 elephant

2 because fish have their own scales

3 clock

4 Cain
Read Cain's story in Genesis 4:1–5.

Words to Practice

old in gold

bold	mold	goldfish	sold
told	hold	cold	fold

-en in sharpen

broken	darken	eaten	given
frozen	lighten	loosen	flatten

-es in peaches

freezes	dishes	houses	lunches
teaches	wishes	reaches	branches

ild in child

childhood   mildest   wildly

ind in kind

behind	find	blind	rind
wind	mind	grind	bind

upon   they're

The Goldfish

Pauline Croll

I have a bowl of goldfish
  Upon my windowsill.
They're just like me, my daddy says,
  They never can keep still.

They're like the gleams of sunshine
  Which make us glad each day.
They're just like me, my mother says,
  I make her feel that way.

Think About It!

Give the correct answer.

*How is the child in this poem like a fish?

68

their	Pharisee	obey	laws
proudly	publican	collect	extra
mercy	forgive		

The Publican's Prayer

Another story that Jesus told was about two men that went to the Temple to pray. One man was a Pharisee. This man was a leader in the Temple and a leader over the

Jewish people that lived during that time. He tried very hard to obey all the laws and to be a good person. Because of that, people gave him respect. When he came to pray, he stood tall and said proudly, "Thank you, God, that I'm *not* like the rest of these people. I don't do bad things like *they* do, and I give all that the law says I should give. I'm glad that I'm not like *that* man there."

The Pharisee looked down at the publican across the room. Publicans would go to homes and collect taxes. People needed to pay their taxes in order to live in their homes.

Sometimes this publican would tell the people they needed to pay two coins when they only needed to pay one. He told them a lie because he wanted the extra coin for himself. The people knew that they could not trust publicans, and they did not like any of them.

On this day, the publican had come to pray as well, but he did not pray like the Pharisee did.

He bowed his head and cried, "God, please have mercy on me. I am a sinner."

This was very different from what the Pharisee said to God. Jesus said that God forgave the publican of his sins, but not the Pharisee.

The Pharisee was proud and did not think he had any sin. So he did not ask for God to forgive him, and God did not forgive him. The publican knew he was a sinner. Because the publican was humble and knew that he needed God to save him from his sin, God forgave the publican and made him His child.

James 4:6

"God resisteth the proud, but giveth grace unto the humble."

Think About It!

Give the correct answer.

*1. Why do you think Jesus told this story?

2. What was wrong with the Pharisee's prayer?

Read Jesus' story in *Luke 18:9–14.*

cherry   kindly

finest   beautiful

Freddy and the Cherry Tree

Freddy saw some fine, ripe cherries
    Hanging on a cherry tree.
And he said, "You pretty cherries,
    Will you not come down to me?"

"Thank you kindly," said a cherry;
    "We would rather stay up here.
If we dared to drop this morning,
    You would eat us up, I fear."

One, the finest of the cherries,
    Dangled from a slender twig.
"You are beautiful," said Freddy,
    "Red and ripe, and oh, how big!"

"Catch me," called the cherry. "Catch me,
    little mister, if you can."
"I would catch you soon," said Freddy,
    "If I were a grown-up man."

Freddy jumped and tried to reach it,
    Standing high upon his toes.
But the cherry bobbed about,
    And laughed, and tickled Freddy's nose.

"Never mind," said little Freddy,
    "I shall have them when it's right."
But a blackbird whistled boldly,
    "I shall eat them all tonight."

Think About It!

Give the correct answer.

1. What did Freddy want the cherries to do?

*2. Why could the blackbird eat the cherries when Freddy could not?

-**y** in rain**y**

bakery	fuzzy	breezy	sandy
sleepy	thirsty	dirty	scratchy

-**er** in bigg**er**

darker	faster	helper	kinder
lighter	smaller	softer	driver

-**est** in bigg**est**

fastest	quickest	slowest	wisest
smallest	longest	tallest	lightest

-**ly** in slow**ly**

costly	kindly	quickly	freely
directly	exactly	firmly	orderly

a in banan**a**

zebra	instant	camera	elephant
extra	panda	comma	umbrella

Wish

Dorothy Brown Thompson

If I could wish,
I'd be a fish
(For just a day or two)
To flip and flash
And dart and splash
And nothing else to do,
And never any one to say,
"Are you quite sure
You washed today?"
I'd like it, wouldn't you?

Think About It!

Give the correct answer.

*1. Why wouldn't the fish need a bath?

*2. Why does the author want to be a fish for just a day or two?

Words to Watch For

airplane	below	ribbon
winding	among	alligator
strange	edge	gone

Bunny and His Airplane

Anna Williams Arnett

"I wish I could fly," said Bunny one day, as he watched the birds flying across the sky.

A long-legged crane standing nearby heard what Bunny said.

Mr. Crane stretched his long neck around. He looked at Bunny and said, "You may never be able to fly, but you can have a ride in the sky."

77

Bunny sat up very quickly. "How can I have a ride in the sky?"

"On my back," said Mr. Crane. "I will fly across the lake in a few minutes. You may go with me, and I'll bring you back on my return trip in an hour."

"How wonderful!" exclaimed Bunny. "I am ready to go any time."

"Very well, but you must put on your little green coat and your red cap and ask your mother if you may go," said Mr. Crane.

Bunny hurried home to ask his mother and to get his coat and cap.

Soon he came hopping back with his coat and cap on.

"Mother says I may go!" shouted Bunny.

"Put your arms around my neck and climb upon my back," said Mr. Crane.

How wonderful it was to be sailing through the air!

The trees and hills were so far below them that people looked like tiny specks.

78

The river looked like a silver ribbon winding among the green hills.

The cool wind swept Bunny's ears back as they rushed through the air.

As they were flying over the lake, Bunny saw something big in the water. He leaned over to see what it could be. He was so interested that he forgot to keep his arms around Mr. Crane's neck, and suddenly down, down went Bunny and dropped— *splash!* into the water.

He landed right on the back of the big
thing. And what do you suppose it was? It
was old Mr. Alligator, who was taking his
afternoon nap.

Well, maybe you think Mr. Alligator
wasn't surprised! He had never before seen
a rabbit, and he didn't like to have this
strange animal riding on his back. But what
could he do?

Then Mr. Alligator thought, "I'll swim over to that big log at the edge of the lake and scratch my back on it. That will knock this animal off, and then I'll gobble him up."

So Mr. Alligator swam over to the edge of the lake.

But Bunny jumped to the log, and hopped to the ground and was gone before you could blink an eye.

That was the last ride in the sky that Bunny ever took.

 **Think About It!**

Give the correct answer.

1. Who helped Bunny fly in the sky?

2. How did Bunny fall on Mr. Alligator's back?

*3. What did the author mean when she said it was Bunny's last ride?

 *Words to Practice*

o in sh**o**vel

above	come	lion	front
done	love	son	mother

c in **c**ity

voices	ice	mice	distance
fence	nice	face	lettuce

ought in th**ough**t, **aught** in c**aught**

taught   fought   daughter   brought

au in f**au**cet, **aw** in s**aw**

author	August	pause	sauce
hawk	fawn	thaw	straw
jaws	paws	gnaw	squawk

ph in **ph**one, **ch** in **ch**orus

alphabet	photo	elephant	dolphin
ache	echo	anchor	character

Words to Watch For

wear   meadow

comical: *funny*

fare: *what someone eats or drinks*

hedge: *a row of bushes*

Grasshopper Green

George Cooper

Grasshopper Green is a comical chap;
    He lives on the best of fare.
Bright little trousers, jacket, and cap,
    These are his summer wear.

Out in the meadow he loves to go,
    Playing away in the sun;
It's hopperty, skipperty, high and low,
    Summer's the time for fun!

Grasshopper Green has a quaint little house;
    It's under the hedge so bright.
Grandmother Spider, as still as a mouse,
    Watches him all through the night.

Gladly he's calling the children, I know,
    Out in the beautiful sun;
It's hopperty, skipperty, high and low,
    Summer's the time for fun!

Think About It!

Give the correct answer.

  *What are fun things you would do in
the summer time?

84

Words to Practice

g in giant, dge in fudge

age	cage	huge	strange
page	giraffe	engine	large
ledge	wedge	bridge	badge

ie in brownie

believe	cookie	field	shield
yield	retrieve	piece	brief

ey in key, ey in obey

honey	donkey	monkey	valley
money	they	prey	survey

ea in leaf, ea in thread, ea in steak

beak	clean	gleam	seal
feather	Heaven	ready	bread
break	weather	great	pleasant

The Pocket

Ilo Orleans

Today when I was at the zoo,
I watched the mother kangaroo.

Inside her skin she has a pocket.
She puts her baby there, to rock it!

Solve these word puzzles.

1 What kind of nut has no shell?

2 The more of them you take,
   the more you leave behind.
   What are they?

3 What can you catch but not throw?

4 My name meant princess,
   but I wasn't one.
   I laughed when God
   told me I would have a son.
   Who am I?

1 doughnut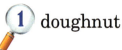

2 footsteps

3 a cold

4 Sarah
Read Sarah's story in Genesis 17:15–18:14.

Twenty Froggies

George Cooper

Twenty froggies went to school
Down beside a little pool,
Twenty little coats of green,
Twenty vests all white and clean.

"We must be on time," said they.
"First we study, then we play;
That is how we keep the rule,
When we froggies go to school."

Master Bullfrog, grave and stern,
Called the classes in their turn;
Taught them how to nobly strive,
Likewise how to leap and dive.

From his seat upon the log,
He showed them how to say, "Ker-chog!"
Also how to dodge a blow
From the sticks that small boys throw.

Twenty froggies grew up fast;
Bullfrogs they became at last.
Not one dull among the lot,
Not one lesson they forgot.

Polished in a high degree,
As each froggie ought to be,
Now they sit on other logs,
Teaching other little frogs.

Think About It!

Give the correct answer.

*1. What are the froggie's coats?

*2. Which school rule is good to
    remember?

Making the Best of It

"What a dreary day this is!" said old Gray Goose to Mrs. Brown Hen.

"Yes, it is a gloomy day," answered Mrs. Brown Hen.

They stood at the henhouse window and watched the snow fall outside. Every corner of the farmyard was turning white.

"I am very hungry," said a duck nearby.

A group of chicks standing huddled together added, "And we are very thirsty!"

The farmer's son usually fed them each day. But today, he did not come. As hour after hour went by, the animals became very unhappy. The cold, winter wind howled around the henhouse.

Now, White Rooster was not like the other animals. He appeared to be quite happy as usual. No other animal in the farmyard ever seemed as content as White Rooster.

"Well," said White Rooster as he looked around the henhouse, "you all seem to be down in the dumps today."

No one answered.

This was too much for White Rooster. He stood first on one foot and then on the other. He turned his head from side to side.

One of the little hens hopped down from her perch. She strutted over to White Rooster.

"When we are full and have had plenty to eat, we are lively," said the little hen. "But when we are starving, we can hardly hold our heads up."

"If I ever see that farmer's son again, I'll peck his foot," squawked another rooster.

"You won't see the farmer's son until he feeds us," replied White Rooster. "Then you'll be busy pecking the corn—not him."

"Oh, don't talk about corn," squawked Mrs. Brown Hen. "I am so hungry."

"I am hungry, too," said White Rooster. "But it could be worse. We could be surrounded by hungry foxes. At least we can stretch our wings."

"That is true," answered Mrs. Brown Hen.

So all the animals in the henhouse stretched their wings and cleaned their feathers and began to look a little happier.

"Now then," crowed White Rooster, "let's have a little music. That will cheer us up and help the long hours pass. We will sing a merry song."

"Would you be so kind as to start a lively tune for us, Mrs. Brown Hen?"

Mrs. Brown Hen shook herself proudly. She tossed her head back and began to sing. In no time, everyone in the henhouse had joined her.

The cows, sheep, and horses were not far away. When they heard the happy voices in the henhouse, they too, joined in the merry song. The pigs did their best to squeal louder than all the rest. The animal chorus got louder and louder as

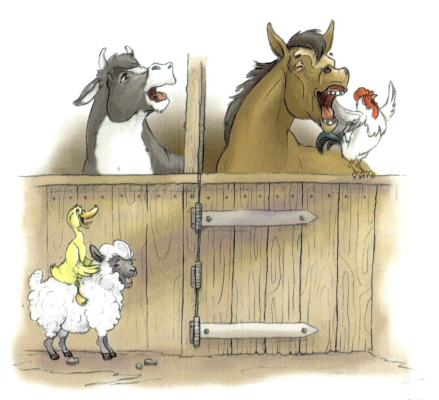

each group tried a little harder. All the animals were so happy that they forgot they were hungry. All at once the door of the henhouse burst open and in marched three little children. Suddenly, the hens were silent.

A little girl wrapped in her thick coat and heavy scarf stepped into the light. Her sweet little face could hardly be seen, but her words were kind. "Don't stop singing," laughed the little girl. "We enjoy your music."

Behind her, two kind boys, each carrying a full dish of tasty chicken food, entered the house. "We were so lonely cooped up inside from the cold," one boy said.

"We heard all of you singing, and we laughed and laughed," the little girl added. "When we went to tell Jack, the farmer's son, about your singing, we found out he was sick. Then Jack told us all about you."

"You poor animals!" the little girl said. "You haven't had anything to eat or drink."

At once, the children happily set the tasty food before the hens.

"Cock-a-doodle-doo!" crowed White Rooster. "All this comes from making the best of things."

Once again the hens began to sing. All the animals joined in happy chorus. Even Jack smiled as he heard the merry music from the farmhouse.

Think About It!

Give the correct answer.

1. Why were the animals sad?

2. How was the white rooster different from the other animals?

*3. How can you be cheerful?

Philippians 4:4

"Rejoice in the Lord alway: and again I say, Rejoice."

care   wrap   cover
knickers: *pants*

Furry Bear

A. A. Milne

If I were a bear,
    And a big bear too,
I shouldn't much care
    If it froze or snew;
I shouldn't much mind
    If it snowed or friz—
I'd be all fur-lined
    With a coat like his!

For I'd have fur boots and a brown fur wrap,
And brown fur knickers and a big fur cap.
I'd have a fur muffle-ruff to cover my jaws,
And brown fur mittens on my big brown paws,
With a big brown furry-down up to my head,
I'd sleep all the winter in a big fur bed.

 **Think About It!**

Give the correct answer.

*Why doesn't the bear mind if it is cold?

Lunchtime at the Zoo

Ilo Orleans

"It's time for lunch,"

The zookeeper said;

"And what would you like today?"

Jumbo, the elephant,

Trumpeted loud,

"Peanuts and lettuce and hay!"

"Now, Mister Sea Lion,"

The zookeeper called,

"Tell me, what is your wish?"

The sea lion blinked,

Then happily barked,

"My wish is a pailful of fish!"

"And you, Mister Hippo?"

The zookeeper asked.

"I'll open my mouth!" Hippo cried,

"And, please, won't you toss a basket of bread

And a bucket of apples inside!"

Think About It!

Give the correct answer.

1. What did the elephant want to eat?

2. Which animal ate fruit?

3. What did the sea lion wish for?

A Funny Dream

Coletta Morrow

Late last night as I lay in my bed,
　　I had such a funny dream.
Something looked so very good—
　　A little house made of ice cream.

A lot of animals passed that way—
　　A hawk, a fawn, a seal.
They all were licking that little house.
　　Oh! What a yummy meal!

Then the sun began to shine—
    The little house started to thaw.
All the animals ran right home
    And quickly came back with a straw!

Think About It!

Give the correct answer.

*Could this dream come true? How do
  you know?

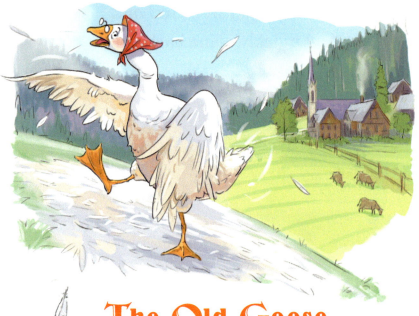

The Old Goose

Helen Wing

I'll tell you a story
    About an old goose
Who waddled so much
    All her feathers came loose.
"My goodness," she cried,
    As she looked all around,
"It's only July, and there's
    Snow on the ground!"

Just Trust Him

Bethany Roberts

Lizzy looked around her empty room. This new home was not *at all* like her old home in Maine. Even her new room looked different. She looked out the window and saw a big field with a wooden fence all the way around it.

Just then, Dad brought some brown boxes into the room. He plopped them on the floor next to her dresser.

"Here you go, Lizzy," he said. "You can start to unpack these clothes. Make sure to leave out one outfit for school tomorrow."

Lizzy started to take some shirts out of the box, but she was still thinking. She would have to go to a new school in the morning, and her friends were back in Maine. When her dad came in with some more boxes, he saw Lizzy's sad face.

"I know it is hard to move to a new place, Lizzy," he said. "What was that verse I read to you this morning?"

"Blessed is the man that trusteth in the Lord."

"That's right," Dad said. "God will help you feel at home here soon. He may even help you make new friends. Just pray and trust Him."

Lizzy nodded and smiled at her dad. She hoped that God would do all those things.

"Why don't we take a break and go explore?" said Dad. "Go get your brother and meet me on the porch."

Lizzy smiled and ran to get Gabe from his room. The two met Mom and Dad on the porch, and they all went for a walk down the dirt road. Lizzy saw that same wooden fence she had seen from her window. The fence was so long that she could not see where it ended. It kept on going over the hill. When they reached the top of the hill, they looked down on the rest of the field.

"What is that over there?" Gabe asked.

"It looks like sheep," Mom chuckled. "It must be a sheep farm."

Across the field, a man turned to face them and waved his hat for them to come.

"Let's go!" Dad said.

They walked down the hill until the field stopped at a little farmhouse. The man who waved his hat came outside the gate to meet them. He looked very kind, and Lizzy liked him already.

"You must be new around here," he said as he shook Dad's hand. "I'm Mr. Sanders. Let me go get my family. They will want to meet you, too."

Mr. Sanders walked to the doorway of the farmhouse and called for his wife and children. Soon a smiling woman came out of the house with two boys. One boy looked to be the same age as Lizzy. The other was Gabe's age. The parents sat down on the porch to talk, but the boys, Danny and Peter, took Lizzy and Gabe to the fence to pet the sheep.

"The sheep are so soft," Lizzy said.

"The little lambs are even softer,"
said Peter.

Then they heard a happy bark, and a
black and brown dog came running from
the barn. It ran up to Gabe and stood up
on its back legs to lick Gabe's face. Gabe
giggled and scratched the dog's ears.

"This is Roxy. She's always happy to meet new friends," said Danny.

"Boys!" Mr. Sanders called from the porch. "It's time for the sheep to come into the barn! Let Roxy in the gate!"

Peter walked over and opened the gate, and Danny went to open the barn door. When Roxy heard the gate open, her ears perked up, and she ran inside. She knew exactly what to do.

"Bring them in, Roxy!" Peter called to her.

Roxy ran around the sheep barking, and the sheep started to move. Roxy ran one way and then the other way until she had chased

the sheep all the way into the barn. Gabe and Lizzy watched in wonder. They had never seen anything like it.

"Wow! What a smart dog!" Lizzy said.

Peter began to tell her about other tricks Roxy could do. As they talked, Lizzy found out that both Danny and Peter would be at her school in the morning.

The sun was beginning to set when they started their walk home. Lizzy looked up at the golden sky and remembered what Dad had said. She smiled to herself. God had helped her begin to feel like she was at home in this brand new place. He even helped her make some great new friends.

Think About It!

Give the correct answer.

*1. Why is it hard to live in a new place?

*2. What things in this story did God use to make Lizzy feel at home?

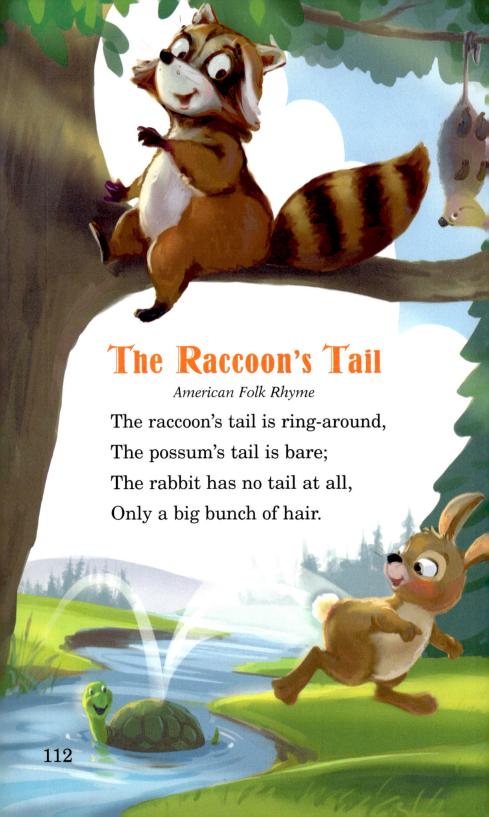

The Raccoon's Tail

American Folk Rhyme

The raccoon's tail is ring-around,

The possum's tail is bare;

The rabbit has no tail at all,

Only a big bunch of hair.

112

Words to Watch For

creature   years

Can You Guess?

Solve these word puzzles.

1 There is an animal kept in a cage,
Often he's growling and roaring in rage.
Beautiful mane and a smooth brown coat,
Which of the animals now gets your vote?

2 What kind of coat can be put on only
when wet?

3 There is a creature who lives in the sea,
Flippers for feet and some whiskers has he.
Funniest bark you have ever heard,
Now can you guess it with only one word?

4 I dreamed of a ladder to Heaven above.
Then worked many years because
I fell in love.
Who am I?

lion

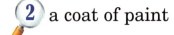 a coat of paint

 seal

 Jacob
Read Jacob's story in Genesis 28.

A Knock in the Night

Sometimes it is easy to think that God doesn't have time for our little needs. We don't pray that God will help us to find our lost book or help us to be a kind friend. We think things like that are too small to pray

115

for. Jesus told a story in the book of Luke that shows us what God thinks about those little things.

There once was a man who lived in a small house with his wife and children. One night, he was tucking his children into bed when there was a knock at his door.

He looked out his window to see his friend standing there. The man did not know why his friend would come to his house so late.

"What do you need?" he said.

"I am out of food, and a guest just came to stay at my house," the friend said. "May I have some bread?"

"It is too late. I have already put my children to bed. I cannot help you now," the man said.

"Oh, please!" the friend called from the outside. "I just need bread. I have nothing to feed my guests."

"No, friend," the man said. "I do not want to wake up my children or my wife. Come back tomorrow."

The man walked away from the window and got back in bed. All was silent for a moment, but then there was a knock again.

"Please?" the friend asked.

The man's children and his wife began to stir. He got up grudgingly and went to the table.

"All right, my friend," he said. "I will give you all the bread you need."

Jesus said the man gave his friend bread because his friend kept asking.

If we keep asking God's help for what we need, even the little things, He will happily give us what we need. God loves us very much and wants to give us good gifts.

Luke 11:9

"And I say unto you, Ask, and it shall be given you; seek, and ye shall find; knock, and it shall be opened unto you."

Think About It!

Give the correct answer.

*1. What is this story mainly about?

    a. a man who doesn't want to get up

    b. a friend who asks his neighbor for bread

*2. Why do you think Jesus told this story?

Read Jesus' story in *Luke 11:5–10.*

enough

A Kitten with a Mitten

Polly Berrien

A kitten with a mitten on
Never did I see.
A kitten with a mitten on
Would never ever be.

A kitten with a mitten on
Should stay out of the snow.
A kitten needs FOUR mittens on.
I'm old enough to know.

Think About It!

Give the correct answer.

*Why wouldn't you see a kitten with a mitten?

119

Words to Watch For

calico   captain   parrot

sailor   boxful

pesky: *bothersome*

One Kitten for Kristy

Adelaide Holl

Kristy was a girl who had too many kittens. Kristy did not think so, but her mother and father did.

"You may keep just one kitten," they told her. "You will have to give the rest of them away. We just can't have a house full of kittens."

Kristy chose the roundest calico kitten for her own. She put the others in a basket and set it inside her wagon. Then away she went with FIVE kittens in her basket.

Mrs. McGinty was sweeping the
sidewalk.

"What beautiful kittens!" she said,
looking into the basket.

"Would you like one?" Kristy asked.

"Indeed, I would," said Mrs. McGinty.
"But, you see, I have some goldfish. A
kitten might eat the goldfish."

"Maybe we could trade," said Kristy.

Mrs. McGinty hurried inside. She came out with a round glass bowl. In it were two golden-orange fish. Kristy was delighted. Mrs. McGinty chose a kitten of snowball-white and set the goldfish in the wagon.

Away Kristy went with FOUR kittens in her basket and two goldfish in a bowl.

She pulled her wagon quietly because she was coming to Miss Murphy's house. Miss Murphy did not like squeaky wagons or noisy children.

"Hello, Miss Murphy," said Kristy. "I have some nice, quiet kittens to give away."

"Did you say quiet kittens?" asked Miss Murphy. "Let's take a look."

She looked into the basket. The kittens were making a purring sound.

"Wait!" Miss Murphy said.

She went inside and came out again with a parrot in a cage.

"This is Skipper," she said. "A sea captain sent him to me. He sings "The Sailor's Hornpipe." Would you like to trade a nice, quiet kitten for a nice, noisy parrot?"

"Oh, yes!" agreed Kristy.

Miss Murphy chose a kitten of smoky-gray. Away went Kristy down the street with THREE kittens in a basket, two goldfish in a bowl, and one green parrot in a cage.

Kristy turned the corner and stopped to watch Mr. Wiggins. He was making mounds of oranges and apples on his fruit stand.

"Pesky mice!" Mr. Wiggins muttered. "They keep nibbling my fruits and cheeses!"

"What you need is a kitten," Kristy told him.

"I could use *two* kittens," Mr. Wiggins said.

He picked up two that were midnight-black. He smiled. "Come, Kristy. Come with me."

Behind the store was a boxful of wiggly brown puppies.

"Take your pick," Mr. Wiggins said.

Kristy chose the puppy with the floppiest ears and the droopiest tail. And away she went with ONE kitten in her basket, two goldfish in a bowl, one green parrot in a cage, and a wiggly, brown puppy in a box. She stopped at Mr. Green's house. He was chasing a shiny, black rooster.

"Pesky rooster!" he shouted. "I'm going to put him in the soup pot! Every morning, he crows and wakes me up!"

"Oh, please don't!" called Kristy. "Give him to me. I'll give you a kitten."

Mr. Green looked pleased.

"That's a fine idea," he said. "My little girl would love this striped kitten for her birthday tomorrow."

He put the rooster in a small crate. And away Kristy went with an empty basket, two goldfish in a bowl, one green parrot in a cage, a wriggly brown puppy in a box, and a shiny, black rooster in a crate.

She felt very happy and proud. When she got home, she called, "Mother! Father! I found a home for every single kitten! Aren't you glad?"

Give the correct answer.

*1. How do you think Kristy's parents reacted to her bringing home more animals?

2. Why was Mr. Green glad to trade his rooster for a kitten?

*3. Which of Kristy's neighbors *needed* a kitten?

a. Miss Murphy

b. Mr. Wiggins

c. Mrs. McGinty

126

Can You Guess?

Solve these word puzzles.

1 What is the longest word in the dictionary?

2 What runs all around the pasture
     yet never moves?

3 We are little airy creatures,
    All of different voice and features,
    One of us in *glass* is set,
    One of us you'll find in *jet,*
    The other you may see in *tin,*
    And the fourth a *box* within.
    If the fifth you should pursue,
    It can never fly from *you.*

4 I had some funny dreams
    that made my brothers mad.
    A coat with many colors
    I was given by my dad.
    Who am I?

127

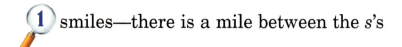 **1** smiles—there is a mile between the *s*'s

2 fence

3 all five vowels—*a, e, i, o, u*

4 Joseph

Read Joseph's story in Genesis 37.

Action

Ilo Orleans

Horses gallop,
Monkeys leap,
Eagles swoop,
And possums—SLEEP!

Panthers pounce
Rabbits hop,
Bullfrogs dive
And donkeys—STOP!

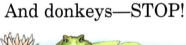

Think About It!

Give the correct answer.

*Can you think of any actions like the ones from the poem that *you* can do well?

129

Missing

A. A. Milne

Has anybody seen my mouse?

I opened his box for half a minute
Just to make sure he was really in it,
And while I was looking, he jumped outside!
I tried to catch him, I tried, I tried. . . .
I think he's somewhere about the house.
Has *anyone* seen my mouse?

*Uncle John, have you seen
   my mouse?*

Just a small sort of mouse,
   a dear little brown one
He came from the country he wasn't a town one,
So he'll feel all lonely in a London street;
Why, what could he possibly find to eat?

130

He must be somewhere. I'll ask Aunt Rose:
Have *you* seen a mouse with a woffelly nose?
Oh, somewhere about—
He's just got out. . . .

Hasn't anybody seen my mouse?

Think About It!

Give the correct answer.

1. How did the mouse get out?

*2. Describe the mouse.

*3. Who was asked first about the mouse? Next?

A Cowboy Legend

Willis Lindquist

When cowboys are out on the range at
night, they like to sit around a campfire
and sing and tell stories. One of the stories
they often tell is about a white stallion that
roams the prairies.

A wild, white horse it was, with silvery
mane and tail, and it could run faster than
the wind.

A big horse, and smart—and the most beautiful horse in the world, cowboys said. And each one that saw it wanted it for his own.

One cowboy named Tex almost did catch that white stallion.

He watched and waited, and one day he saw the stallion drinking water from a pool.

It was a deep pool of spring water.

Tex built a fence around that pool, and he left the gate wide open. Then he hid and he waited.

But the beautiful, white horse was too smart. It saw the fence, and it stopped going to that water hole.

Tex waited. The dry season came, and all the water holes dried up. All except that one, which was fed by springs. Tex waited, for he knew the white horse would soon have to come there to drink.

And at last, one day, the stallion did come to the pool. It went right inside the fence, and Tex quickly shut the gate. Then he gave a whoop—the white horse was his at last!

The sun had set, and Tex knew that it was too dark to lasso the horse that night. He would have to leave it until morning.

But in the morning, the horse had gone. The great, strong horse had smashed right through the gate!

Sadly, Tex turned away.

Many cowboys had tried to catch that wild horse before, and many more tried after Tex.

134

But to this day, no one has caught the beautiful white stallion of the prairies. Free and wild it roams, and it runs faster than the wind.

Think About It!

Give the correct answer.

*Number these sentences in the order they happened in the story.

____ Tex caught the horse.

____ Tex built a fence around the pool to catch the wild, white horse.

____ The horse broke the gate and ran off.

____ Tex watched and waited for the wild, white horse.

The Rainbow

Christina Rossetti

Boats sail on the rivers,
    And ships sail on the seas;
But clouds that sail across the sky
    Are prettier far than these.
There are bridges on the rivers,
    As pretty as you please;
But the bow that bridges heaven,
    And overtops the trees,
And builds a road from earth to sky,
    Is prettier far than these.

Words to Watch For

Alto	Ohio	embarrassing
improved	colonel	grocer
musicians	signal	cornetist
piccolo	indignant	

Lentil

Robert McCloskey

In the town of Alto, Ohio, there lived a
boy named Lentil. Lentil had a happy life
except for one thing—he wanted to sing,

but he couldn't! It was most embarrassing, because when he opened his mouth to try, only strange sounds came out . . . and he couldn't even whistle because he couldn't pucker his lips.

But he did want to make music so
he saved up enough pennies to buy a
harmonica. Lentil was proud of his new
harmonica and he decided to become an

expert. So he played a lot, whenever and wherever he could.

His favorite place to practice was in the bathtub, because there the tone was improved one hundred percent.

He used to play almost all the way to school. Down Vine Street to the corner of Main, past the finest house in Alto, which belonged to the great Colonel Carter, then

past the drug store, the barber shop, and the Alto Library, which was a gift of the great Colonel Carter, by the Methodist church, through the Carter Memorial Park, and around the Soldiers and Sailors Monument that the Colonel had built there.

Then Lentil would stuff his harmonica into his pocket and take a shortcut up

the alley behind the hardware store so he would not be late for school.

People would smile and wave hello to Lentil as he walked down the street, because everyone in Alto liked Lentil's music; that is, everybody but Old Sneep. Old Sneep didn't like much of anything or anybody. He just sat on a park bench and whittled and grumbled.

One day the news got around that the great Colonel Carter, who had been away for two years, was coming home.

People began to plan a grand welcome, but when Old Sneep heard the news he said: "Humph! We wuz boys together. He ain't a mite better'n you or me and he needs takin' down a peg or two."

Sneep just kept right on whittling, but everybody else kept right on planning. Colonel Carter was the town's most important citizen, so the people hung out flags and decorated the streets. The mayor prepared a speech, and the Alto Brass Band put on their new uniforms, and the printer, the grocer, the plumber, the minister, the barber, the druggist, the ice man, the school teachers, the housewives and their husbands and their children—yes, the whole town went to the station to welcome Colonel Carter.

The train pulled in. The musicians in the band were waiting for the leader to signal them to play, the leader was waiting for the mayor to nod to him to start the band, and the mayor was waiting for Colonel Carter to step from his private car. All the people held their breath and waited.

Then there was a wet sound from above. There sat Old Sneep, sucking on a lemon.

Old Sneep knew that when the musicians looked at him their mouths would pucker up so they could not play their horns.

The whole band looked up at Old Sneep. The mayor gave the signal to play, but the cornetist couldn't play his cornet, the

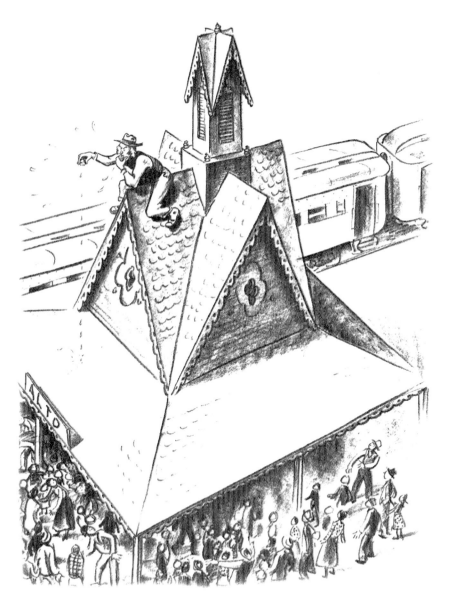

piccolo player couldn't play his piccolo, the
trombone player couldn't play his trombone,
and the tuba player couldn't play his tuba,
because their lips were all puckered up.

They couldn't play a single note! The
musicians just stood there holding their
instruments and looking up at Old Sneep
sucking on the lemon.

The leader looked helpless, the people
were too surprised to move or say a thing,
and the mayor wrung his hands and
wore a look that said: "Can't somebody do
something, please!"

As Colonel Carter stepped
from his car, the only sound
was the noise of Sneep's

SHLISH!

lemon. Clouds began to gather on the colonel's brow and he said: "Hmph" in an indignant sort of way.

Of course Lentil's lips were not puckered and he knew that something had to be done. So he took out his harmonica and started to play "Comin' 'round the Mountain When She Comes."

When Lentil began to play the second chorus, Colonel Carter smiled. Then he let out a loud chuckle and began to sing "Driving Six White Horses When She Comes."

Then everybody sang and they all marched down Main Street behind the colonel's car. Lentil rode with the colonel, who took a turn at the harmonica when Lentil's wind began to give out. (He said that he hadn't played one since he was a boy, but he did very well considering.)

They marched to the colonel's house and paraded through the gate onto the front lawn.

The mayor's committee served ice cream cones to all the citizens and Colonel Carter made a speech saying how happy he was about such a fine welcome and how happy he was to be home again. When he said that he was going to build a new hospital for the town of Alto, everybody was happy— even Old Sneep!

So you can never tell what will happen when you learn to play a harmonica.

Think About It!

Give the correct answer.

*1. What is the story mainly about?

   a. an old man who was unhappy

   b. a marching band

   c. a boy who wanted to play music

   d. the homecoming of Colonel Carter

2. What news did Colonel Carter give that made everybody happy—even Old Sneep?

Plot—Sequencing

Write two to three sentences summarizing the beginning, middle, and ending of "The Tenth Husky."

Beginning

Sasha ran after a bunny.

Middle

She went on the

Ending

Her master rescued her.

Drawing the Plot

Draw a scene from the story.

CREDITS